Maths Challenge

Games
Book

LEVEL 2

David Kirkby

WALKER BOOKS
LONDON

Parents' notes

The National Curriculum

AGE 5yrs → 12yrs

NATIONAL CURRICULUM LEVEL

| 1 | 2 | 3 | 4 | 5 |

Mathematics is one of three core subjects within the National Curriculum. The National Curriculum covers the age-range 5–16, and children start at Level 1, with some eventually reaching the top Levels, 8, 9 and 10.

Children will be capable of performing at different levels. For example, a child who is performing mostly at Level 2 will be able to do some activities at Level 3, and perhaps even something at Level 4.

The mathematics curriculum has been divided into 14 areas known as "Attainment Targets" which can be grouped under these headings:

Using and applying mathematics
Number
Algebra
Measures
Shape and space
Data handling

Maths Challenge and the National Curriculum

Maths Challenge is aimed at children within the age-range 5–13 and provides support for children who are already working from Level 1 through to Level 5 at school

At each Level there are two books – an Activity Book and a Games Book. These are best used in conjunction with each other.

The Activity Book provides mathematical activities across a spectrum of the curriculum, the Games Book contains a collection of mathematical games to consolidate and supplement these ideas.

The contents of the books at each level cover a cross-section of the curriculum. Detailed guides are given to parents relating each activity to particular Attainment Targets within the National Curriculum.

The Maths Challenge series contains:

Activity Books Levels 1 – 5
Games Books Levels 1 – 5

First published 1991 by Walker Books Ltd
87 Vauxhall Walk, London SE11 5HJ
© 1991 David Kirkby   Reprinted 1991
Printed and bound in Hong Kong
by Dai Nippon Printing Co. (HK) Ltd
British Library Cataloguing in Publication Data
A catalogue record for this title is available from
the British Library.
ISBN 0-7445-1884-9

Using the Books

Maths Challenge consolidates the mathematical ideas children have met in school. The ideas are presented here in a lively and stimulating way, to provide an enjoyable learning experience.

Parents can do a lot to support work that their child's school will be covering in mathematics. Do not worry if your child does not pick up the ideas straightaway. Here are some suggestions of ways you can contribute to your child's learning experience through Maths Challenge.

The Activity Books

* Help your child interpret the tasks by talking through the activity with them.
* Ask them to explain some things to you – this is a good way of helping them to learn with more understanding.
* Discourage your child from rushing through the book – one activity per day is sufficient, or even one per week, or when the mood is right.
* Encourage children to do the Challenges – these are an important component of each activity. Sometimes it may be possible to involve other members of the family in these.
* Praise your child frequently for their effort and do not let them worry about making mistakes.

The Games Books

* Help your child interpret the rules.
* All games require two players unless otherwise stated, so here is an opportunity for you to play with your child and observe their mathematical development.
* In some games it may be possible to involve several members of the family.
* Encourage your child to try the Challenges – these often require varying the rules and sometimes gives him or her valuable practice at working alone.
* Discourage children from rushing through the book – it is a good idea to return to the games, particularly those they enjoyed.
* You will need some simple pieces of apparatus:
  2 dice
  a pack of playing cards (Ace counts as 1)
  counters (You can make these from coloured paper. For most games, players must use one colour to avoid confusion.)

Parents' notes

Each activity relates to a combination of different attainment targets outlined in the National Curriculum. These are given in brackets underneath the headings.

1 Halving and doubling

(Number, Algebra)

This game reinforces the idea of "odd" and "even", together with "halving" and "doubling". A variation might be to use a shuffled pack of playing cards 1–10, and take a card from the pile instead of throwing the dice.

2 Catch a fish

(Number)

This activity practises finding both the total and the difference of the numbers on two dice. You can give your child further practice by pointing to a fish and asking him or her to arrange the faces of the two dice to "catch a fish".

3 Shape cover

(Shape and space)

"Shape cover" encourages identifying shapes by their names. Before starting the game you could spend some time matching the names to the shapes. Why not extend the activity by pointing to different shapes around the house and asking for their names?

4 Dice and cards

(Number, Shape and space)

This game gives your child practice in addition. Another variation might be to allow each player to throw two dice and then choose which dice number to add to the card number.

5 Change game

(Number, Measures)

Here your child can gain experience in adding small sums of money and calculating the change required from 10p. If further practice is needed try pointing to different groups on the page and asking for the total sum of money in each group.

6 Fill a box

(Number, Algebra, Using and applying)

"Fill a box" provides practice of addition and subtraction skills. Give further practice by pointing to different boxes on the sheets and asking for the missing number to fill the box.

Parents' notes

7 Bank

(Number, Measures, Using and applying)

If you have several players then it is a good idea to allow them to take it in turns to be banker – this gives the banker plenty of experience in handling money.

8 Feeding the cats

(Shape and space, Using and applying)

If this game seems too easy change the objective to feeding 4 cats.

9 House

(Number, Shape and space)

This game practises addition skills. The game can be continued until one player has managed to cover his or her whole board with counters.

10 Flowers

(Number, Algebra)

Another game to develop addition skills. You can provide further practice for your child by selecting a card and then seeing how many pairs of flowers can be covered from the one card.

11 Card game

(Numbers)

Add an extra ingredient to the game by also allowing a player to collect two cards if the card difference matches the dice total.

12 Stepping stones

(Number, Algebra)

This game reintroduces the ideas of "odd" and "even". A possible variation is to make a player miss a turn if they land in the river or the swamp.

13 Guess

(Number, Data handling)

If your child has enjoyed this game play a variation by scoring points for guessing the correct difference between the two card numbers.

14 Square shade

(Number, Shape and space, Using and applying)

To save having to draw grids you could make two large 6 x 6 boards and use counters instead of shading.

1   Halving and doubling

You will need:
1 dice
1 counter each

START

Each player places a counter at the START.
Take turns to throw the dice.
If the dice number is EVEN, halve it and
move forward that number of spaces.

move forward 3 SPACES.

★ Challenge ★

FINISH

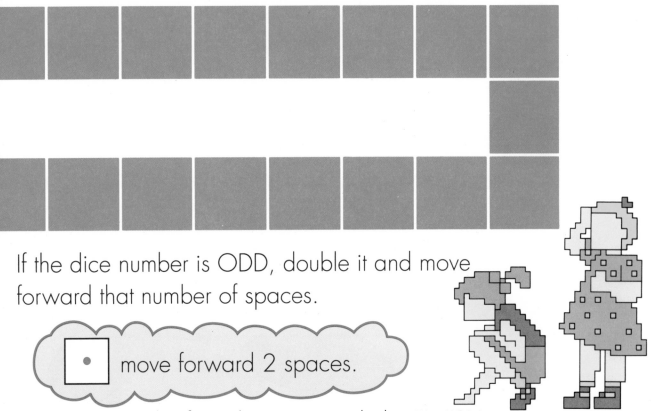

If the dice number is ODD, double it and move forward that number of spaces.

move forward 2 spaces.

The winner is the first player to reach the FINISH.

Play a variation of this game:
If the dice number is ODD, ADD 3 then halve it.

2 Catch a fish

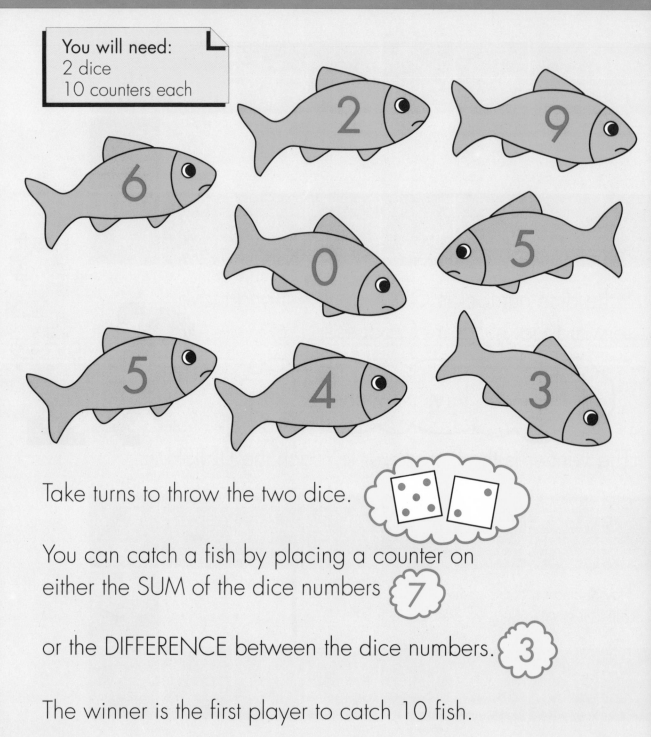

You will need:
2 dice
10 counters each

Take turns to throw the two dice.

You can catch a fish by placing a counter on either the SUM of the dice numbers 7

or the DIFFERENCE between the dice numbers. 3

The winner is the first player to catch 10 fish.

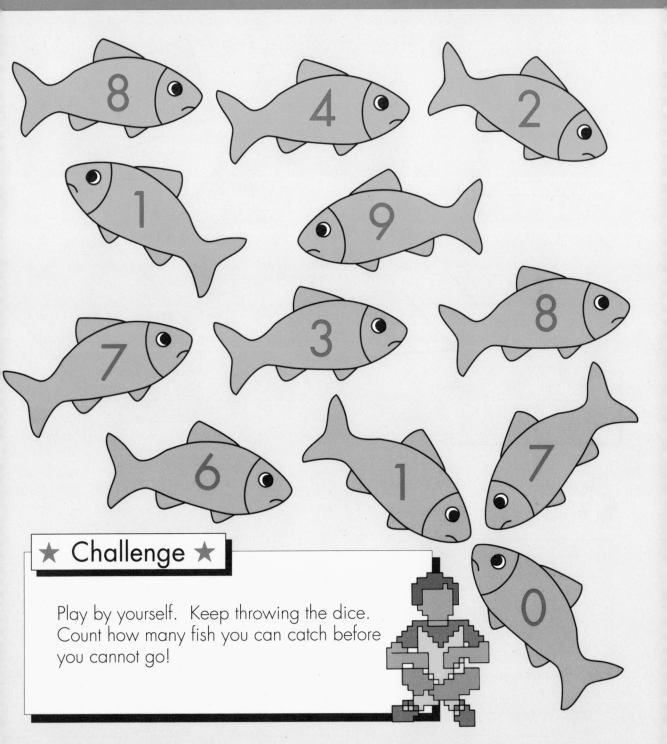

★ Challenge ★

Play by yourself. Keep throwing the dice. Count how many fish you can catch before you cannot go!

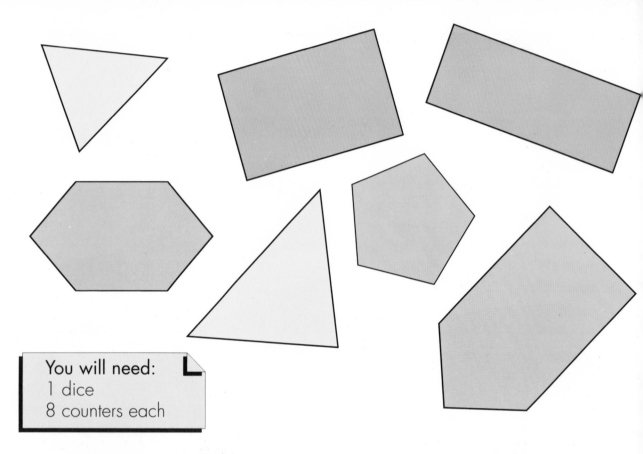

You will need:
1 dice
8 counters each

Take turns to throw the dice. Put a counter on a shape according to this table:

		SHAPE
DICE NUMBER	1	Circle
	2	Rectangle
	3	Triangle
	4	Square
	5	Pentagon
	6	Hexagon

You cannot put a counter on a shape already covered.

The winner is the first player to place all 8 counters.

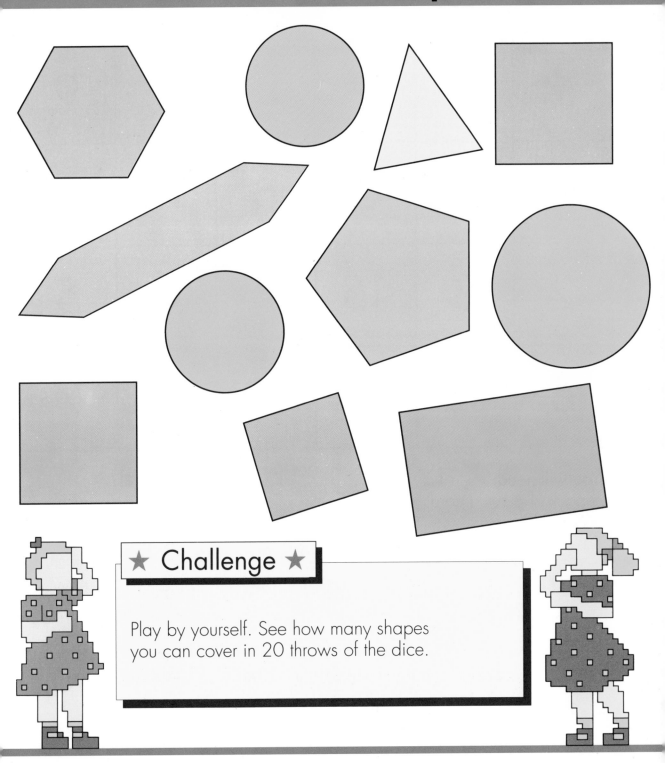

★ Challenge ★

Play by yourself. See how many shapes
you can cover in 20 throws of the dice.

14	5	9	13	8	9
7	10	3	6	16	8
2	8	15	7	4	5
6	12	9	10	11	7

You will need:
a pack of playing cards
1 dice
20 counters each

Choose one board each.
Use all the cards numbered 1–10.
Shuffle them and place them in a pile,
face down. Take turns to turn over the top card, and throw
the dice. ADD together the dice number and the card number.
Place a counter on a square which matches this total.
The winner is the first player to make a row of 6 counters
across.

6	9	5	7	8	2
7	13	3	8	11	10
8	9	10	15	9	14
16	5	6	12	4	7

★ Challenge ★

Play by yourself and see how many squares you can cover with a pile of 25 cards.

You will need:
a pack of playing cards
20 counters each

Use all the cards numbered 1–9.
Shuffle the cards and place them
in a pile face down.

Take turns to turn over the top card.

This card number is the price in pence for some sweets.

Place a counter on each coin in a group which represents
your CHANGE from 10p when you buy those sweets.

For example, card number ⚃, price 4p.

Change from 10p = 6p. So cover 5p 1p or 2p 2p 2p

When all the coins have been covered

the winner is the player who has placed the most counters.

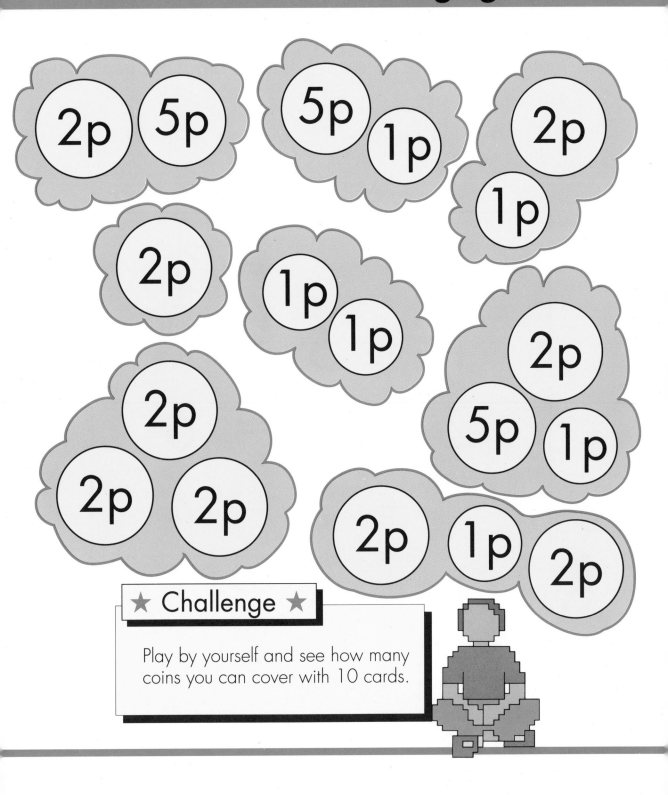

★ Challenge ★

Play by yourself and see how many coins you can cover with 10 cards.

You will need:
1 dice

Play the EASIER GAME first. Each player copies the game card
Take turns to throw the dice and, if possible, fill a box with the
dice number to make a correct line.

The winner is the first player to fill 5 boxes correctly.

Then try the HARDER GAME.

EASIER GAME

$$1 + \boxed{} = 2$$

$$1 + 5 = \boxed{}$$

$$2 + \boxed{} = 6$$

$$\boxed{} + 2 = 4$$

$$1 + 4 = \boxed{}$$

$$\boxed{} + 1 = 4$$

★ Challenge ★

Invent your own game cards and play the game. Remember, the numbers which go in the boxes must be in the range 1–6.

HARDER GAME

5 − ☐ = 4

☐ − 3 = 2

5 − 2 = ☐

6 − 1 = ☐

6 − ☐ = 2

☐ − 3 = 3

7 Bank charges

FINISH | 1p | 5p | 1p | 3p | 2p | 2p | 1p | 7p

4p

1p

4p | 2p | 2p | 6p | 6p | 3p | 1p | 10p

3p

3p

4p | 4p | 3p | 5p | 3p | 10p | 2p | 7p

4p

7p

START | 8p | 1p | 4p | 5p | 6p | 2p | 5p | 6p

You will need:
Several coins
(1p, 2p, 5p, 10p, 20p)
1 dice
1 counter each

One player is the BANKER. Each player starts with 20p.
Take turns to throw the dice and move your counter the
number of squares shown by the dice number.
If your counter lands on a RED square then you PAY the
amount shown to the bank.
If your counter lands on a GREEN square then you COLLECT
the amount shown from the bank.

The winner is the player with the most money when each
has passed the FINISH.

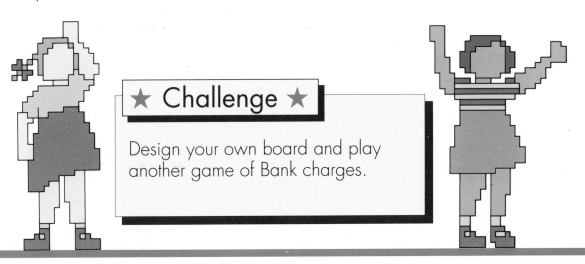

★ Challenge ★

Design your own board and play
another game of Bank charges.

8 Feeding the cats

Take turns to feed one cat.
Do this by placing a counter
in its bowl.

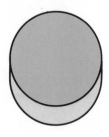

The winner is the first player to feed 3 cats
who are in a line next to each other.

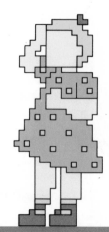

★ **Challenge** ★

Play a variation in which the first player to feed
3 cats who are in a line next to each other loses.

9 House

You will need:
a pack of playing cards
16 counters each

7+1	5+5	1+3	2+7
6+2	3+5	4+2	9+1
4+1	3+4	2+8	2+2
3+2	2+5	6+3	3+3

2+4	8+2	2+3	3+7
1+6	4+3	5+1	8+1
2+2	2+5	7+2	4+1
3+1	5+3	3+6	2+6

This game can be played by four people.
Each player chooses a board. Use all the cards numbered 3–10.
Shuffle them and place them in a pile, face down. The top card
is turned over. Each player places a counter on a square on
his/her board if the sum inside matches the card number.
Continue turning cards over one at a time and placing counters.
The winner is the first player to make a straight line of
4 counters in any direction.

6+1	1+3	1+8	3+3
5+4	2+2	3+6	6+2
2+3	4+6	3+4	1+4
1+5	5+5	4+4	7+3

5+5	4+2	3+1	6+4
3+3	2+4	1+9	4+3
1+7	2+2	4+4	4+5
1+4	3+2	6+3	5+2

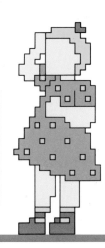

★ Challenge ★

Play by yourself. Deal out 10 cards and
see how many counters you can place.

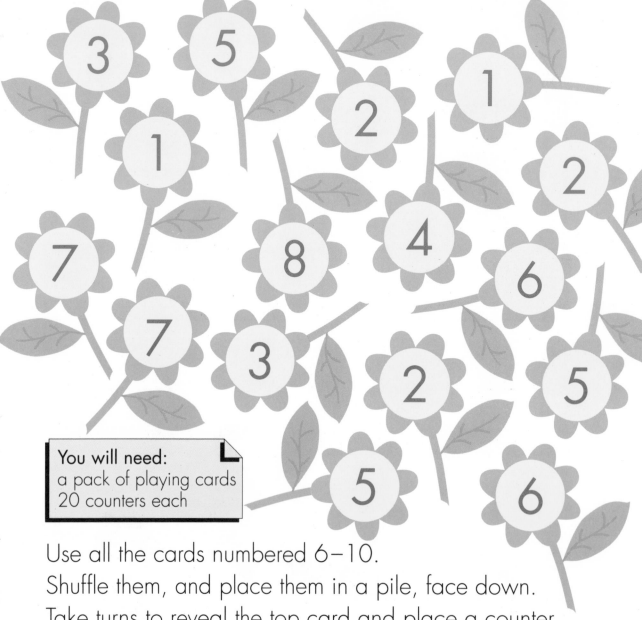

You will need:
a pack of playing cards
20 counters each

Use all the cards numbered 6–10.
Shuffle them, and place them in a pile, face down.
Take turns to reveal the top card and place a counter
on two flowers whose total matches the card number.
The first player unable to cover two flowers loses.

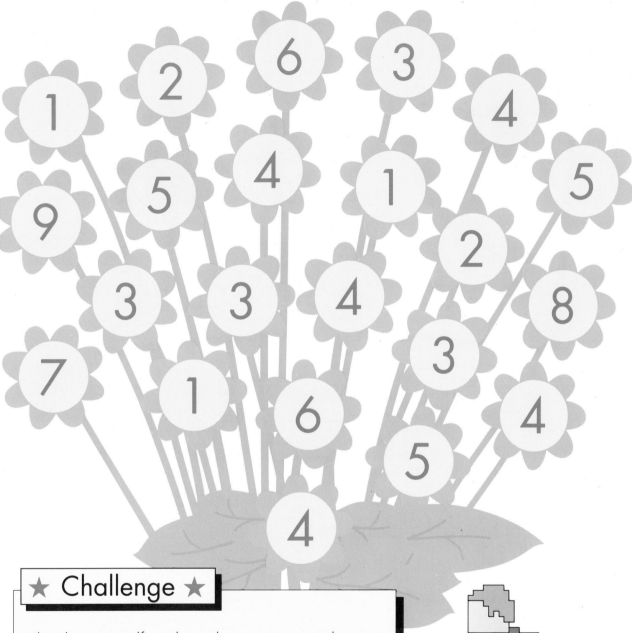

★ Challenge ★

Play by yourself and see how many cards
you turn over before you can't go.

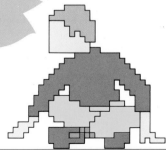

HEARTS

CLUBS

You will need:
a pack of playing cards
2 dice

Use the cards numbered 1–6 in their separate suits.
Shuffle each set and place them in a pile, face up, in their
positions. Take turns to throw the two dice.
When you can see two cards whose total matches the dice
total then collect the two cards. Otherwise do nothing.
Continue until no more cards can be removed.
The winner is the player who has collected the most cards.

DIAMONDS

SPADES

★ Challenge ★

Play by yourself and see how many
cards you can collect from 10 throws
of the dice.

12 Stepping stones

You will need:
2 dice
1 counter each

START

FINISH

swamp

★ Challenge ★

Design your own
Stepping stones game
and play on it using
the same rules.

river with crocodiles

One player chooses to be ODD, the other to be EVEN. Each player places a counter on START. Take turns to throw both dice. If the dice total is an even number, EVEN moves forward that number of stones. If the dice total is an odd number, ODD moves forward that number of stones. The winner is the first player to reach FINISH.

13 Guess

You will need:
a pack of playing cards
20 counters

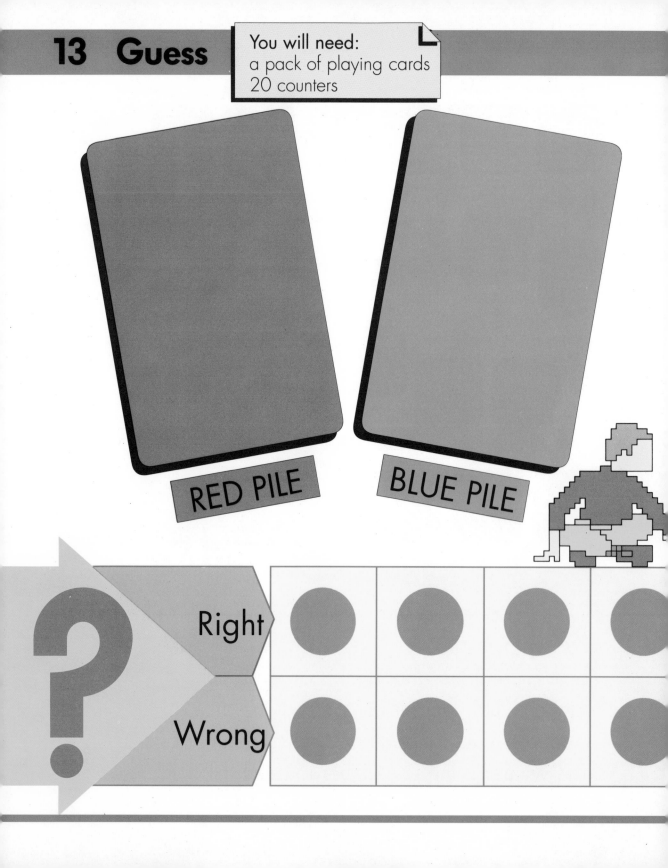

RED PILE

BLUE PILE

?

Right

Wrong

Use two sets of cards, 1–10.

Shuffle the cards and make two piles, face down – a red pile and a blue pile.

Turn over the top card from the blue pile. Guess if the top card on the red pile is MORE or LESS. Turn over the top card from the red pile to see if you are right or wrong.

Place a counter in the right or wrong row. Do the same for the next cards, and continue until all ten pairs of cards have been uncovered. Count the number of correct guesses. Now it is someone else's turn to see if they can do better.

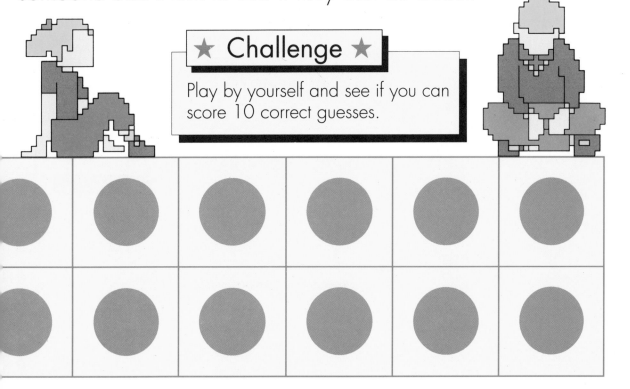

★ Challenge ★

Play by yourself and see if you can score 10 correct guesses.

14 Square shade

You will need:
1 dice
coloured pencils

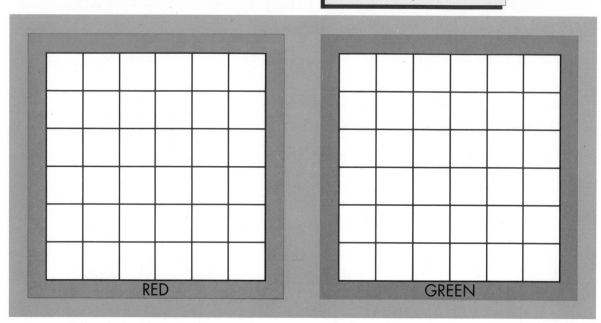

RED   GREEN

One player chooses the RED board, the other the GREEN board. Take turns to throw the dice. Shade a row of squares across according to the dice number.

For example  means you shade a row of 4 squares across

You must shade the exact number of squares. You cannot shade some squares in one row and some in another. If you cannot go miss a turn. The winner is the first player to completely shade his/her board.

★ Challenge ★

Draw some more boards on squared paper and play again. Experiment with boards of different sizes.